**For all portable keyboards** *by Kenneth Baker.*

# THE COMPLETE KEYBOARD PLAYER

## BOOK 2

D0531139

**Wise Publications**
London/New York/Sydney/Cologne

Exclusive Distributors:
**Music Sales Limited**
8/9 Frith Street, London W1V 5TZ, England
**Music Sales Pty. Limited**
120 Rothschild Avenue, Rosebery, NSW 2018, Australia

This book © Copyright 1984 by
Wise Publications
UK ISBN 0.7119.0595.9
UK Order No. AM 38316

Music Sales complete catalogue lists thousands of
titles and is free from your local music book shop,
or direct from Music Sales Limited.
Please send £1 in stamps for postage to
Music Sales Limited, 8/9 Frith Street, London W1V 5TZ.

Printed in England by
Halstan & Co. Ltd., Amersham, Bucks.

# ABOUT THIS BOOK

In Book Two of The Complete Keyboard Player you take a giant step forward in reading musical notation.

Side by side with the single-finger chords, you continue your study of "fingered" chords, by far the most rewarding aspect of left hand accompaniment playing.

As the book progresses you play more and more fill-ins, double notes, and chords with your right hand, which helps give you that "professional" sound.

Although Book Two (like Book One of the series) is designed basically as a "teach yourself" method, teachers everywhere will find it ideal for training tomorrow's electronic keyboard players.

# SHARPS, FLATS, AND NATURALS

**1** This sign is a sharp: ♯

When you see a sharp written alongside a note, play the nearest available key (black or white) to the RIGHT of that note:—

written:

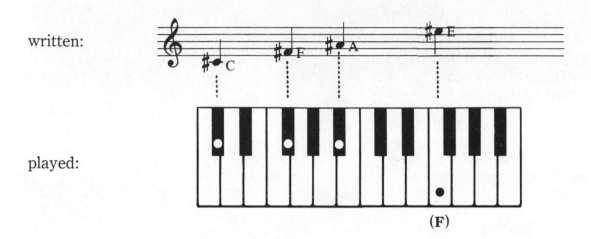

played:

(F)

**Note:** E sharp is simply an alternative way of writing "F".

This sign is a flat: ♭

When you see a flat written alongside a note, play the nearest available key (black or white) to the LEFT of that note:—

written:

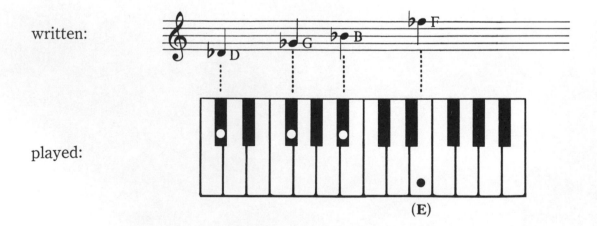

played:

(E)

**Note:** F flat is simply an alternative way of writing "E".

When a sharp or flat is written it
continues as a sharp or flat right through
the bar:—

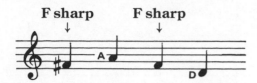

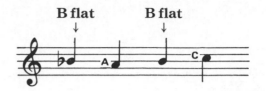

At the next bar, however, everything
returns to normal:—

Apart from at the new bar, a sharp or flat
may be cancelled any time by a sign
called a "natural", ♮ :—

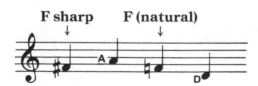

Look out for sharps, flats, and naturals in
the pieces which follow.

# GET BACK

Words & Music by John Lennon & Paul McCartney

**Suggested registration:** electric guitar

**Rhythm:** rock
**Tempo:** medium ( ♩ = 120)

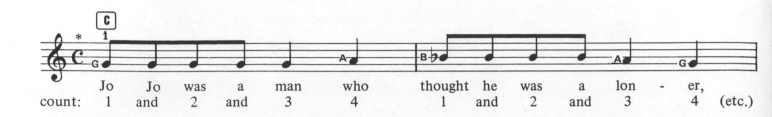

Jo Jo was a man who thought he was a lon - er,

count: 1 and 2 and 3 4 1 and 2 and 3 4 (etc.)

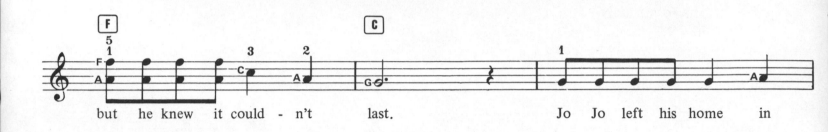

but he knew it could - n't last. Jo Jo left his home in

Tuc - son, Ar - i - zo - na, for some Cal - i - for - nia grass. Get back!

Change finger on G

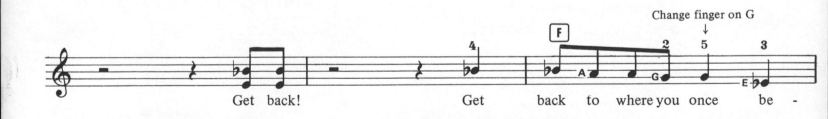

Get back! Get back to where you once be -

longed. Get back! Get back! Get

**\* Common Time.** An alternative way of writing 𝄴

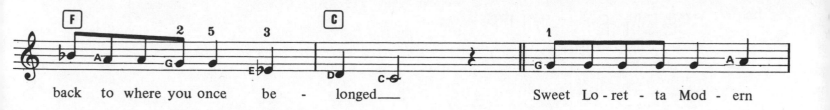

back to where you once be - longed___ Sweet Lo - ret - ta Mod - ern

thought she was a wo - man, but she was an - oth - er man.

All the girls a - round her say she's got it com - ing, but she gets it while she

can. Get back! Get back! Get

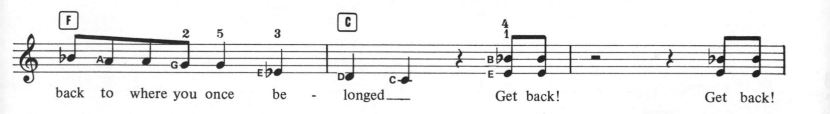

back to where you once be - longed___ Get back! Get back!

Get back to where you once be - longed.___

**\* Pause (Fermata).** Hold the note(s) longer
than written (at the discretion of the performer).

# FOR ONCE IN MY LIFE

Words by Ronald Miller
Music by Orlando Murden

**Suggested registration:** piano + string
ensemble.  Arpeggio optional

**Rhythm:** samba
**Tempo:** medium ( ♩ = 108)
Synchro-start, if available

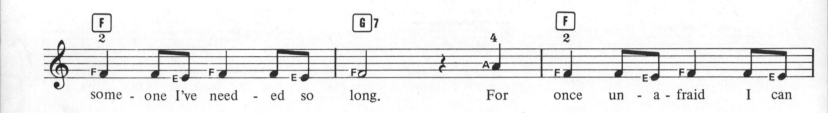

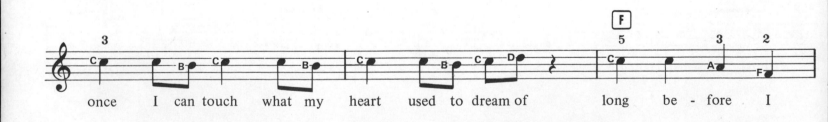

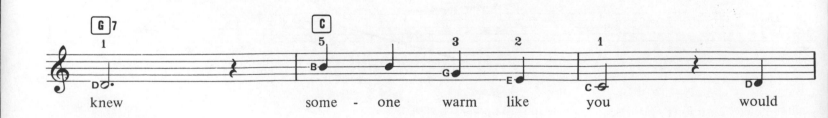

make my dream come true. For once in my life I won't

let sor - row hurt me —— not like it's hurt me be - fore. For

once I have some -thing I know won't de-sert me, and I'm not a - lone an - y -

more. For once I can say this is mine, you can take it,——

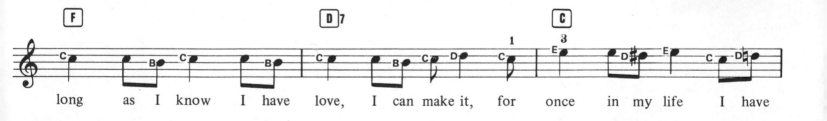

long as I know I have love, I can make it, for once in my life I have

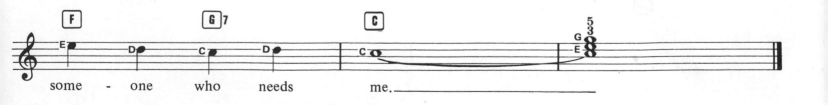

some - one who needs me._____

# ROCK AROUND THE CLOCK

Words & Music by Max C. Freedman & Jimmy
de Knight

**Suggested registration:** trumpet, or saxophone

**Rhythm:** swing
**Tempo:** fairly fast ( ♩ = 160)

Press rhythm start button (ordinary, not
synchro) with left hand, as right hand
strikes first note. Play through Verse
using melody and drums only. Start left
hand chords at Chorus.

**VERSE**

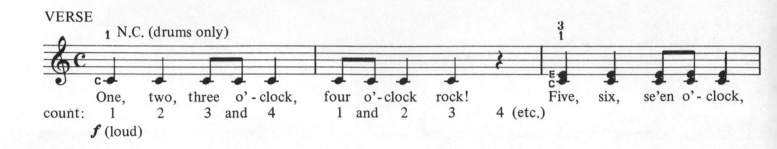

One, two, three o'-clock, four o'-clock rock! Five, six, se'en o'-clock,

count: 1 2 3 and 4 1 and 2 3 4 (etc.)

*f* (loud)

eight o'-clock rock! Nine, ten, 'leven o'-clock, twelve o'-clock rock, we're gon - na

rock a - round the clock to - night! Put your glad rags on,

CHORUS

join me hon, we'll have some fun when the clock strikes one, we're gon - na

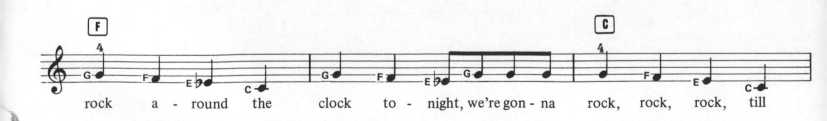

rock a - round the clock to - night, we're gon - na rock, rock, rock, till

broad day - light, we're gon - na rock, gon - na rock a - round the clock to -

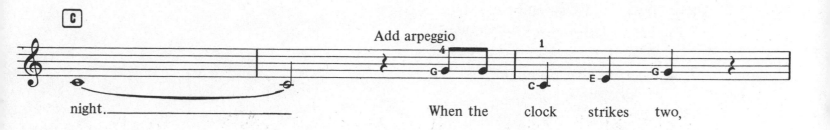

night. ___ When the clock strikes two,

three and four, if the band slows down we'll yell for more, we're gon - na

rock a - round the clock to - night, we're gon - na rock, rock, rock till

broad day - light, we're gon - na rock, gon - na rock a - round the clock to -

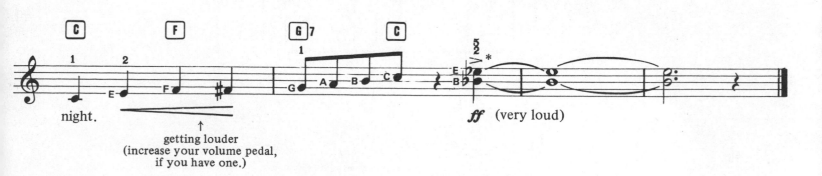

night.

getting louder
(increase your volume pedal,
if you have one.)

*ff* (very loud)

\* ACCENT

# TWO NEW CHORDS: C7 AND A7

**2**

Using single-finger chord method:

Locate "C" and "A" in the accompaniment section of your keyboard. Convert these notes into "C7" and "A7" (see Book One, p. 42ff., and your owner's manual).

Using fingered chord method:

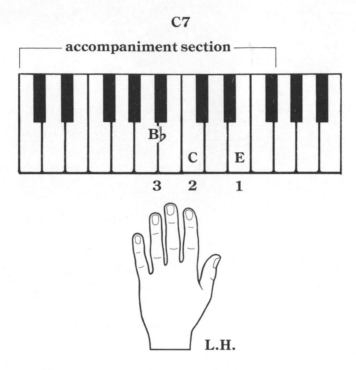

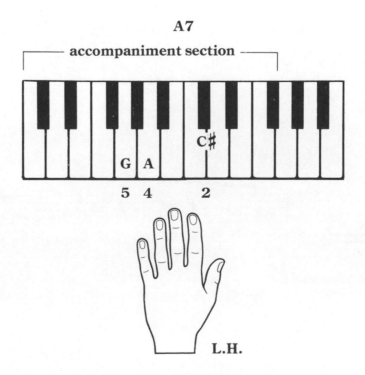

# A NEW STAGE IN READING MUSIC

**3** Up to now, in order to help you, letter names have appeared beside the written notes. These letters will now be discontinued.

Here's how you can learn the names of the notes:

The stave consists of five lines:—

remember this sentence:
**E**very **G**ood **B**oy **D**eserves **F**ruit

and four spaces:—

remember this word: **F A C E**

Learn the notes on the five lines, and the notes in the four spaces first. Then learn the "in-between" notes, like this:

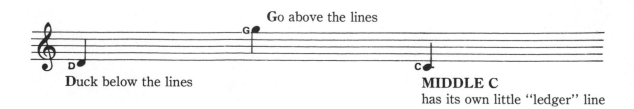

Go above the lines

Duck below the lines

**MIDDLE C**
has its own little "ledger" line

# LET HIM GO, LET HIM TARRY

Traditional

**Suggested registration:** flute

**Rhythm:** bossa nova
**Tempo:** medium ( ♩ = 108)
Synchro-start, if available

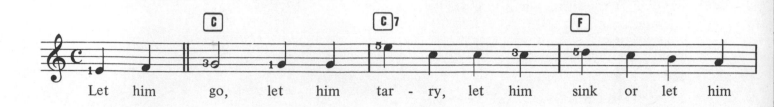

Let him go, let him tar - ry, let him sink or let him

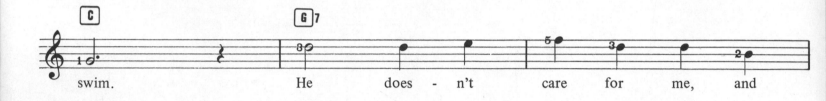

swim. He does - n't care for me, and

I don't care for him. He can go and get an -

oth - er that I hope he will en - joy. For

I'm going to mar - ry a far nic - er boy.

# LOVE ME TENDER

Words & Music by Elvis Presley & Vera Matson

**Suggested registration:** string ensemble.
Arpeggio optional.

**Rhythm:** rock
**Tempo:** medium ( ♩ = 96)

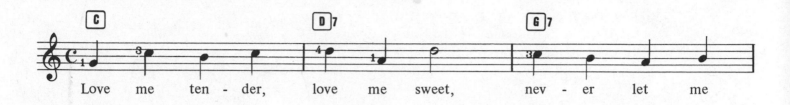

Love me ten - der, love me sweet, nev - er let me

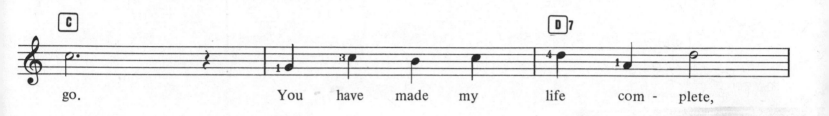

go. You have made my life com - plete,

and I love you so. Love me ten - der,

love me true, all my dreams ful - fil.

For, my dar - lin', I love you, and I al - ways will.

# DAL SEGNO AL CODA (D.S. AL CODA)

**4** A **Coda** is a section, usually quite short, added to a piece of music to make an ending.

**Dal Segno al Coda (D.S. al Coda)** means go back to the sign: 𝄋 and play through the same music again, until:

to coda ⊕

From here jump to CODA and play through to the end.

## SOMETHIN' STUPID

Words & Music by C. Carson Parks

**Suggested registration:** accordion

**Rhythm:** cha-cha (or rhumba)
**Tempo:** medium ( ♩ = 112)
Synchro-start, if available

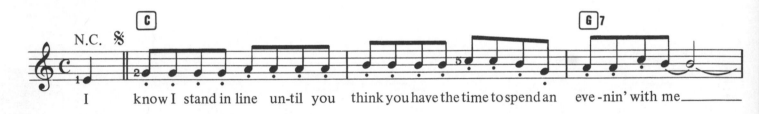

I know I stand in line un-til you think you have the time to spend an eve -nin' with me _____

_ And if we go some place to dance I know that there's a chance you won't be

leav - in' with me. _____ Then af - ter - wards we drop in - to a

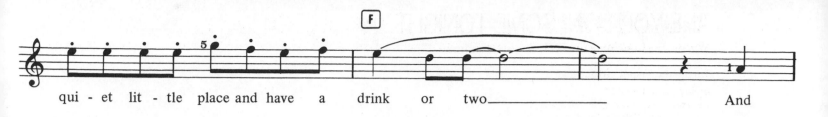

qui - et lit - tle place and have a drink or two_____ And

then I go and spoil it all by say - in' some-thin' stu - pid like "I love you."_____

Change accordion to clarinet

_____ I can see it in your eyes that you des - pise the same old lies you heard the

night be - fore_____ And though it's just a line to you, for

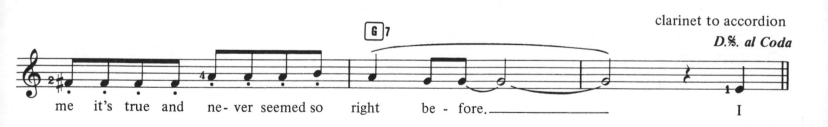

clarinet to accordion
*D.%. al Coda*

me it's true and ne - ver seemed so right be - fore._____ I

⊕ *CODA*

love you."

*f*

# ARE YOU LONESOME TONIGHT

Words & Music by Roy Turk & Lou Handman

**Suggested registration:** flute + full sustain

**Rhythm:** waltz
**Tempo:** fairly slow ( ♩ = 80)
Synchro-start, if available

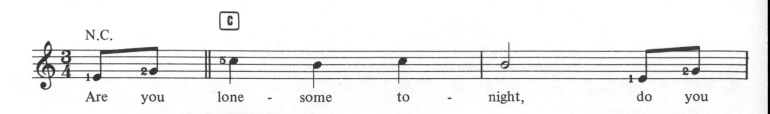

Are you lone - some to - night,   do you

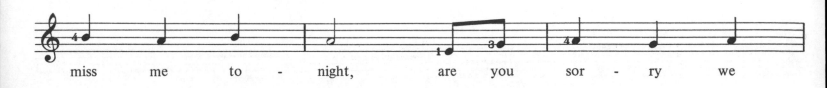

miss me to - night,   are you sor - ry we

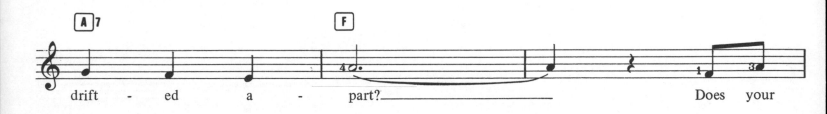

drift - ed a - part?_____   Does your

mem - or - y stray   to a bright sum - mer

day,   when I kissed you and called you "Sweet -

heart?" Do the chairs in your

par - lour seem emp - ty and bare, do you

During rest move 2nd finger up

gaze at the door - step and pic - ture me

Cross 2nd finger over thumb

there? Is your heart filled with pain? Shall I

During rest, move hand up

come back a - gain? Tell me dear, are you

Tuck thumb under 2nd finger

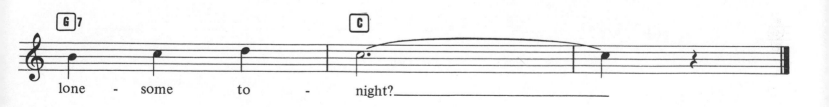

lone - some to - night?

# AN APPLE FOR THE TEACHER

Words by Johnny Burke
Music by James V. Monaco

**Suggested registration:** trombone, or horn

**Rhythm:** swing
**Tempo:** fairly fast ( ♩ = 176)
Synchro-start, if available

An ap-ple for the teach-er, that

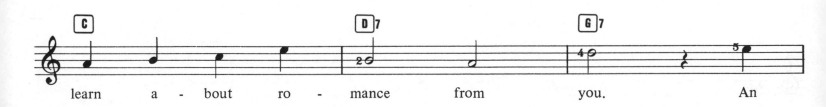

seems the thing to do, be - cause I need to

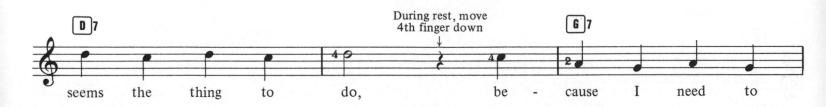

learn a - bout ro - mance from you. An

ap - ple for the teach - er, to show I'm meek and

mild. If you in - sist on say - ing that I'm

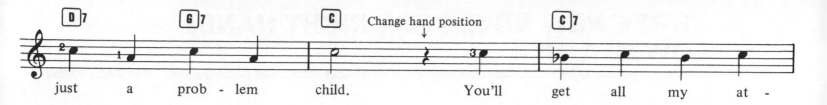

just a prob - lem child. You'll get all my at -

ten - tion, your wish will be my rule; and

may - be you'll be good to me and keep me af - ter

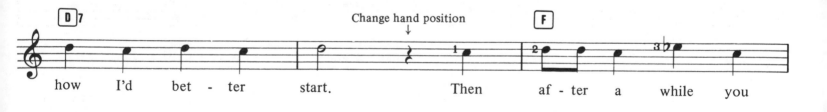

school. An ap - ple for the teach - er, that's

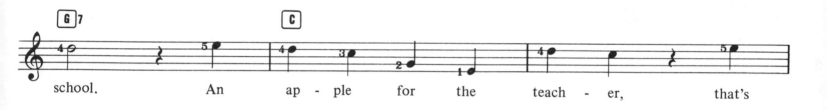

how I'd bet - ter start. Then af - ter a while you

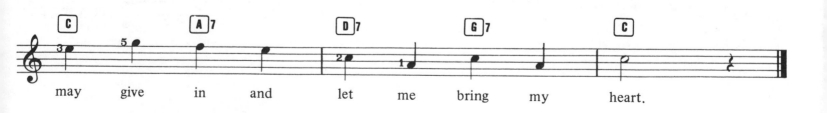

may give in and let me bring my heart.

# THREE NEW NOTES FOR RIGHT HAND: LOW G, A, B

**5**

These three notes lie directly to the left of Middle C. The lowest of them, G, probably forms the left hand extremity of the "melody section" on your instrument.

I have placed letter names beside the new notes only in the next few songs.

## GUANTANAMERA

Words by Jose Marti
Music adaptation by Hector Angulo & Pete Seeger

**Suggested registration:** flute, + duet (if available)

**Rhythm:** bossa nova
**Tempo:** medium ( ♩ = 100)

Guan - ta - na - me - ra___ gua - ji - ra Guan - ta - na - me - ra___
count:  1    2 and 3 and 4    1  2   3 and 4 and    1    2 and 3 and 4 (etc.)

Guan - ta - na - me - ra, gua - ji - ra Guan - ta - na - me -

Change hand position

ra! Yo soy un hom - bre sin - ce - ro___ De don - de

cre - ce la pal - ma.____ Yo soy un hom - bre sin - ce - ro____

De don - de cre - ce la pal - ma____ Y an - tes de

mo - rir - me quie - ro, E - char mis ver - sos del al -

ma. Guan - ta - na - me - ra____ gua - ji - ra

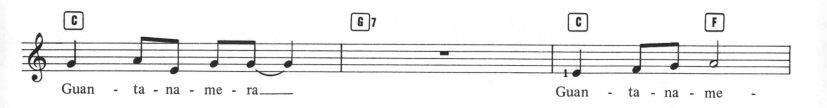

Guan - ta - na - me - ra____ Guan - ta - na - me -

ra, gua - ji - ra Guan - ta - na - me - ra!

# BILL BAILEY WON'T YOU PLEASE COME HOME

Traditional

**Suggested registration:** piano, or honky-tonk
    piano

**Rhythm:** swing
**Tempo:** fairly fast ( ♩ = 176)

New hand position

"Won't    you    come    home,    Bill    Bai - ley?

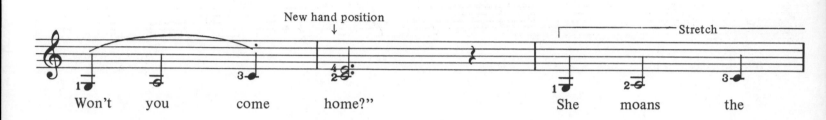

New hand position

Stretch

Won't    you    come    home?"    She    moans    the

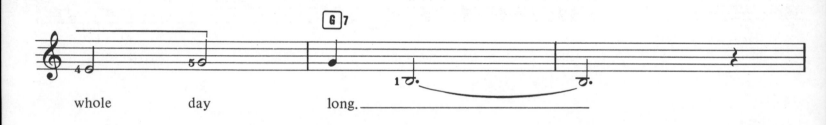

whole    day    long.

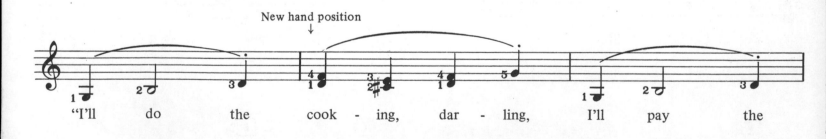

New hand position

"I'll    do    the    cook - ing,    dar - ling,    I'll    pay    the

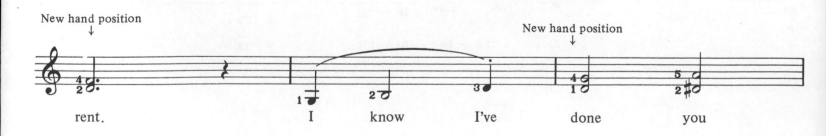

New hand position                    New hand position

rent.                    I    know    I've    done    you

wrong _____ 'Mem - ber that

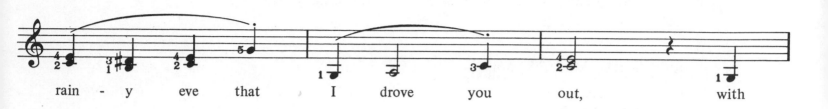

rain - y eve that I drove you out, with

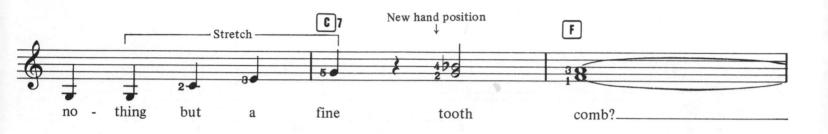

no - thing but a fine tooth comb?_____

— I know I'm to blame, well,

ain't that a shame? Bill Bai - ley won't you

please come home?" home?"

# DA CAPO AL CODA (D.C. AL CODA)

**6** **Da Capo** means "from the beginning".

**Da Capo al Coda (D.C. al Coda)**
means go back to the beginning of the
piece and play through the same music

again, until: to coda ⊕

From here jump to CODA and play
through to the end.

## THIS NEARLY WAS MINE

Words by Oscar Hammerstein II
Music by Richard Rodgers

**Suggested registration:** string ensemble

**Rhythm:** waltz
**Tempo:** slow ( ♩ = 80)

One   dream in my heart
One   girl for my dream
Now,   now I'm a - lone

One   love to be
One   part - ner in
Still   dream - ing of

liv - ing for.   One
par - a - dise   This
par - a - dise   Still

*To Coda* ⊕

love to be liv - ing for.
pro - mise of par - a - dise.
say - ing that

This   near - ly was mine
This   near - ly was mine

26

# MINOR CHORDS

**7** The MINOR CHORD is another important type of chord.

When using the single-finger chord function, there are various ways of forming minor chords. Your owner's manual will tell you how to form minor chords on your particular instrument. The first two diagrams in 8, on the next page, show two possibilities.

# CHORD OF F MINOR (Fm)

**8** Using single-finger chord method:

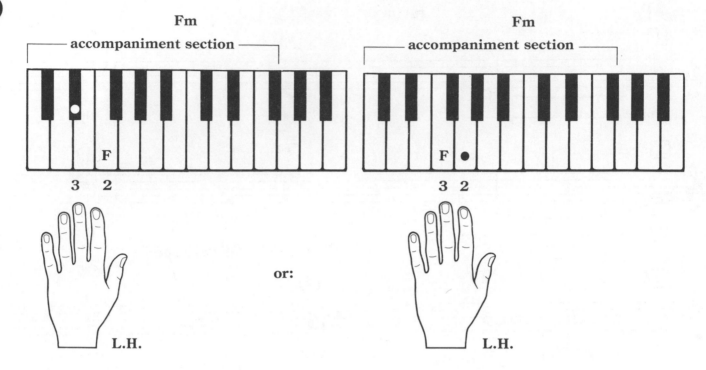

| | or: | |
|---|---|---|
| play F, together with any black note to its **LEFT**. | | play F, together with any (one) note to its **RIGHT**. |

Using fingered chord method:

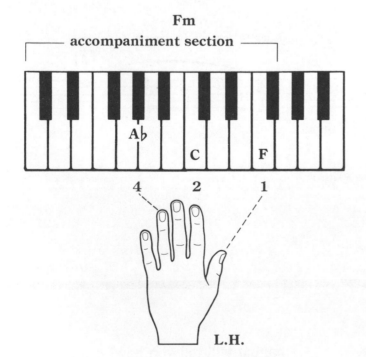

# DOTTED TIME NOTES

**9** A dot after a note adds half as much time again to that note:—

|  |  | lasting |
|---|---|---|
| ♩ | half note (minim) | 2 beats |
| ♩. | dotted half note (dotted minim) | 2 + 1 = 3 beats |
| ♩ | quarter note (crotchet) | 1 beat |
| ♩. | dotted quarter note (dotted crotchet) | 1 + ½ = 1½ beats |

# DOTTED QUARTER NOTE (DOTTED CROTCHET)

**10** A Dotted Quarter Note, ♩., worth 1½ beats, usually combines with an Eighth Note (Quaver), ♪, worth ½ beat, to make two whole beats:—

♩.　♪　　1½ + ½ = 2 beats

or:　♪　♩.　　½ + 1½ = 2 beats

The first of these two time note combinations: ♩. ♪ is the more common. This is how you count it:—

WHAT KIND OF FOOL AM I, p.30

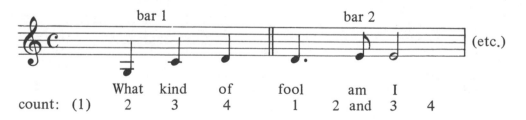

Notice how the "dot" delays note D, so that the next note (E) falls on an "and" beat. The situation is always the same with this rhythm.

Look out for other examples of dotted quarter note/quaver combinations in the songs which follow.

# WHAT KIND OF FOOL AM I

Words & Music by Leslie Bricusse & Anthony Newley

**Suggested registration:** piano

**Rhythm:** bossa nova
**Tempo:** medium ( ♩ = 100)
Synchro-start, if available

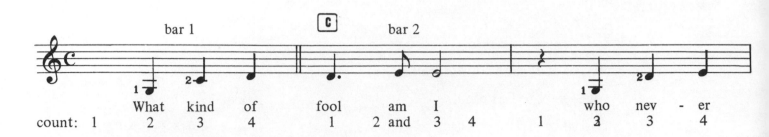

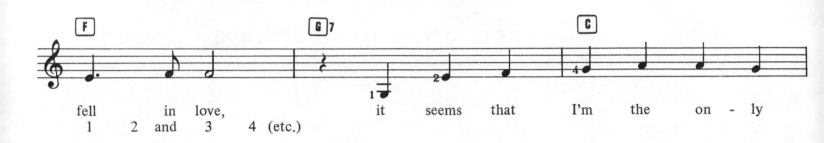

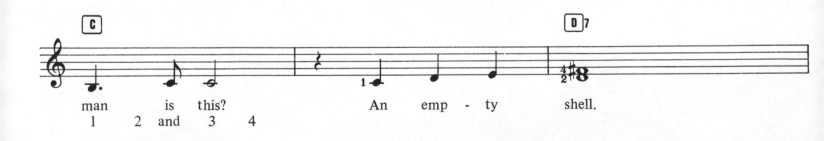

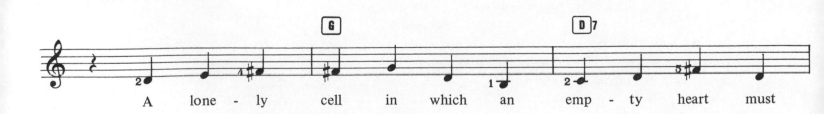

**change piano to trumpet**

dwell.     What kind of lips are these
                    1    2   and   3    4

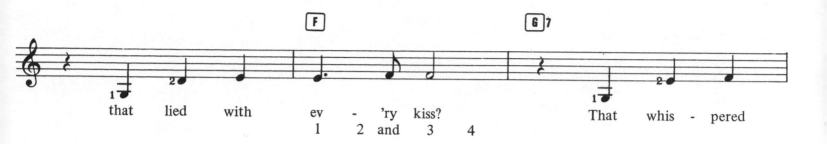

that lied with ev - 'ry kiss?      That whis - pered
         1    2   and   3    4

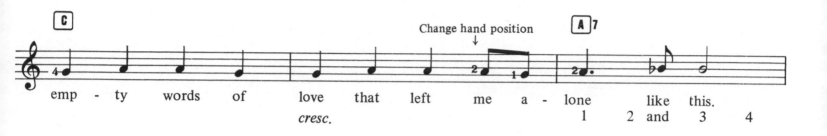

**Change hand position**

emp - ty words of love that left me a - lone like this.
      *cresc.*                               1    2   and   3    4

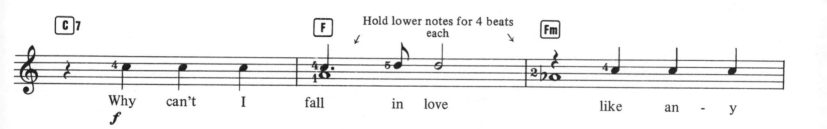

**Hold lower notes for 4 beats each**

Why can't I fall in love      like an - y
 *f*

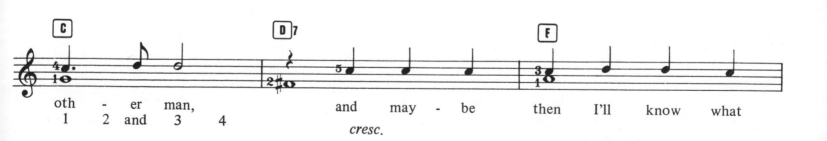

oth - er man,      and may - be then I'll know what
1    2   and   3    4              *cresc.*

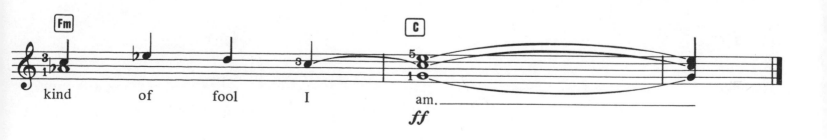

kind of fool I      am. _____
                             *ff*

# LOVE'S ROUNDABOUT
## (LA RONDE DE L'AMOUR)

French Words by Louis Ducreux
English Words by Harold Purcell
Music by Oscar Straus

**Suggested registration:** accordion
+ arpeggio (if available)

**Rhythm:** waltz
**Tempo:** fairly fast ( ♩ = 160)

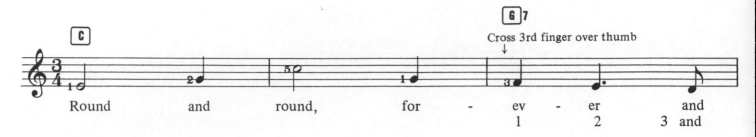

Round and round, for - ev - er and
1    2    3  and

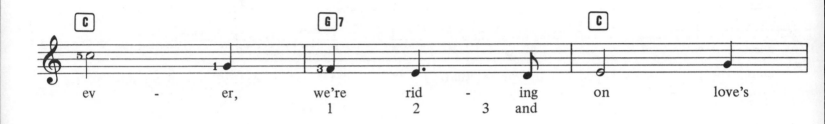

ev - er, we're rid - ing on love's
1    2    3  and

round - a - bout; rich or

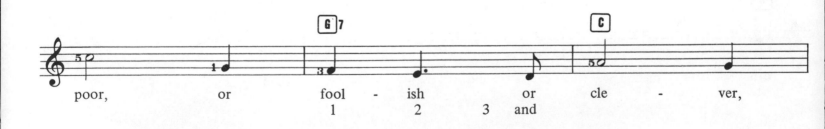

poor, or fool - ish or cle - ver,
1    2    3  and

round we must go, year in, year
1    2    3  and

Change accordion to clarinet

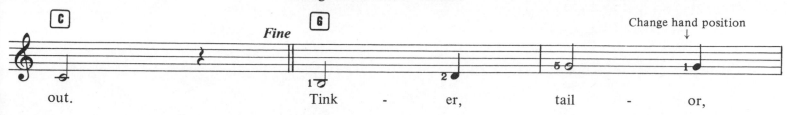

out.                 Tink - er,        tail - or,

sol - dier,      or       sail - or.        Dream     as       the
1          2     3   and              1       2     3   and

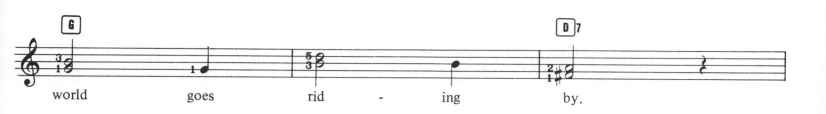

world        goes        rid - ing       by.

Turn       the        pag - es      back    thro'     the
                                           1      2     3   and

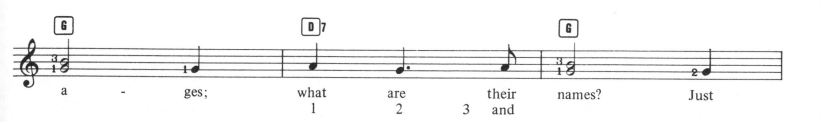

a - ges;      what     are     their    names?     Just
                  1      2     3   and

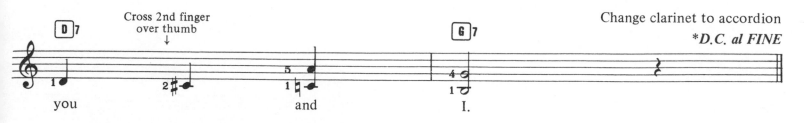

you                       and        I.

* **Da Capo Al Fine.** Go back to the beginning
of the piece and play through the same music
again until FINE (the end).

# STARDUST

Words by Mitchell Parish
Music by Hoagy Carmichael

**Suggested registration:** vibraphone, or celeste,
+ full sustain

**Rhythm:** swing
**Tempo:** fairly slow ( ♩ = 80)
Synchro-start, if available

count: 1   2   3   and 4   and   1   2   3   4   (etc.)

Some-times I        won - der   why   I   spend the   lone - ly

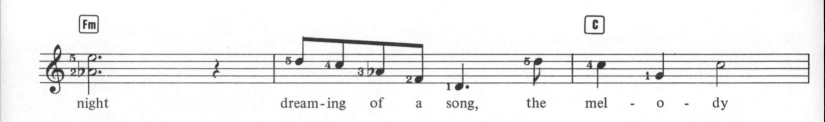

night                dream-ing  of  a  song,   the  mel - o - dy

haunts my  re - ve - rie.        And  I  am once a - gain with   you.        When our

love  was  new,              and each kiss  an  in - spi - ra - tion_____

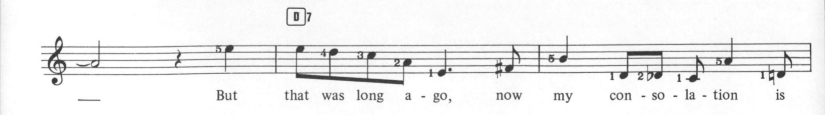

_____   But   that was long a - go,   now  my  con - so - la - tion  is

in the star-dust of a song. Be - side a gar - den

wall when stars are bright, you are in my arms. The

night - in - gale tells his fai - ry tale of par - a - dise where ro - ses

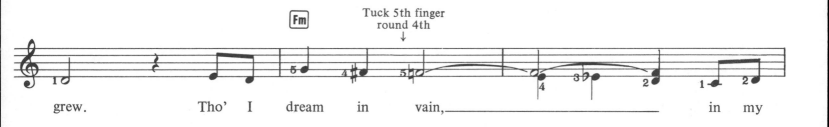

grew. Tho' I dream in vain, _____ in my

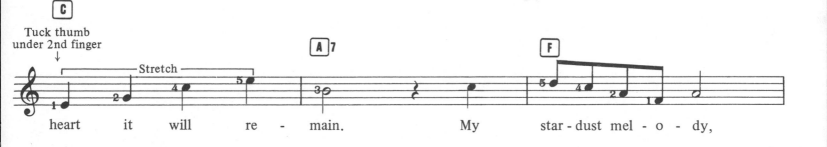

heart it will re - main. My star - dust mel - o - dy,

the mem - o - ry of love's re - frain.

# CHORD OF D MINOR (Dm), AND CHORD OF A MINOR (Am)

**11**

Using single-finger chord method:

Locate D (the higher one), and A, in the accompaniment section of your keyboard. Convert these notes into "Dm" and

"Am" respectively (see Book two, P. 28, and your owner's manual).

Using fingered chord method:

**Dm**

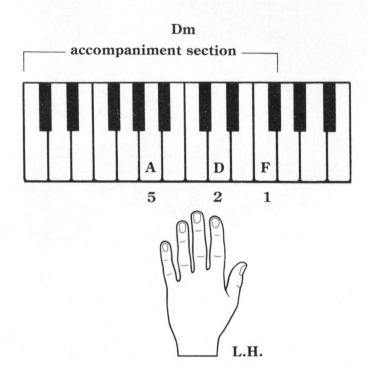

**Am**

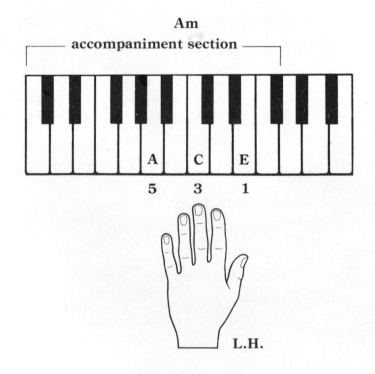

# SCARBOROUGH FAIR

Traditional

**Suggested registration:** flute

**Rhythm:** waltz
**Tempo:** slow ( ♩ = 84)

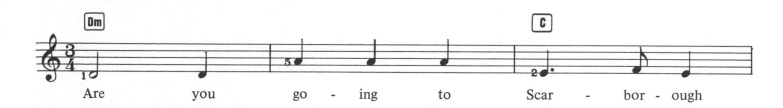

Are you go - ing to Scar - bor - ough

fair? Pars - ley, sage, rose -

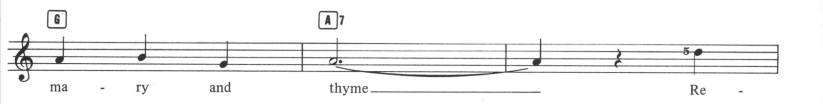

ma - ry and thyme_____ Re -

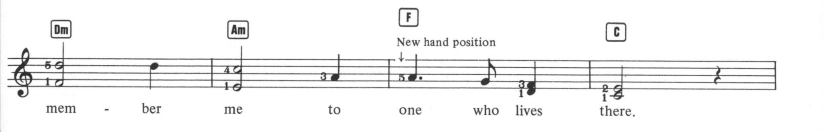

New hand position

mem - ber me to one who lives there.

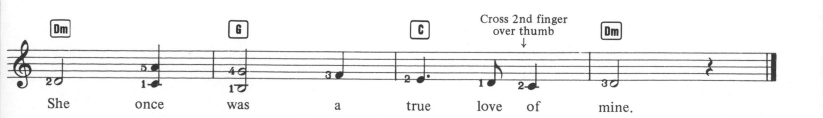

Cross 2nd finger over thumb

She once was a true love of mine.

# TAKE ME HOME, COUNTRY ROADS

Words & Music by Bill Danoff, Taffy Nivert &
John Denver

**Suggested registration:** piano, or electric piano
+ half sustain

**Rhythm:** swing
**Tempo:** quite fast ( ♩ = 192)

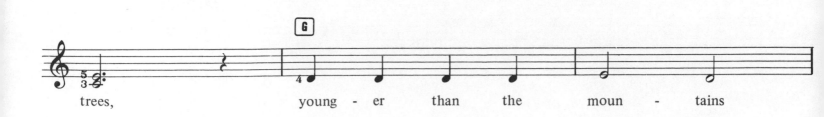

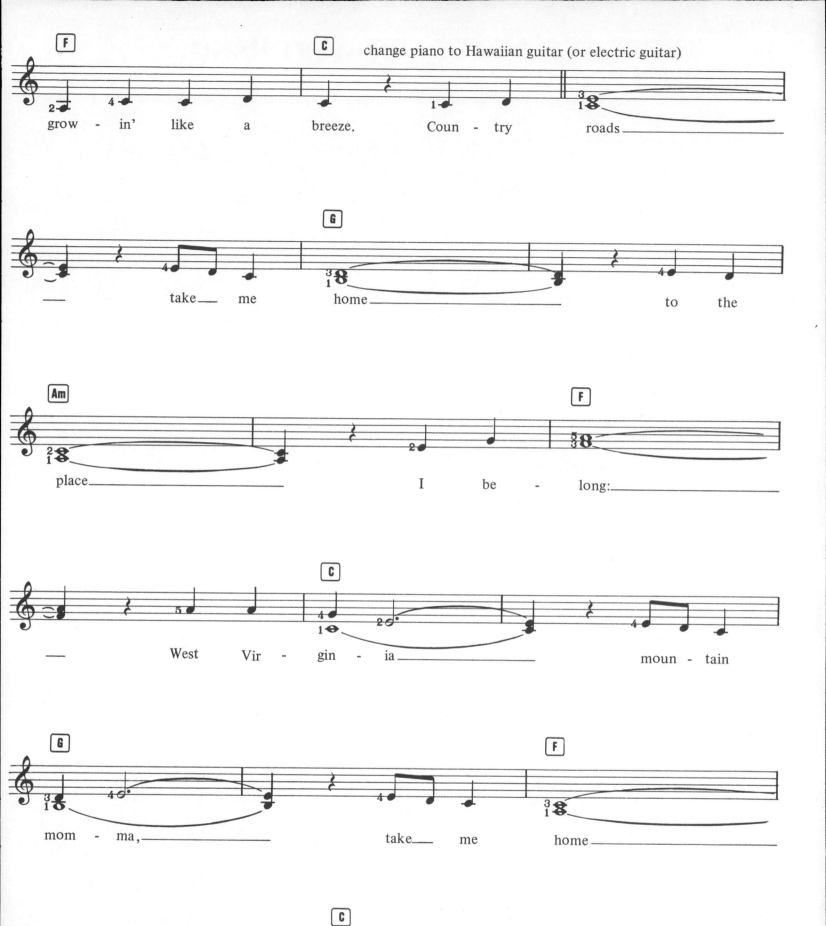

change piano to Hawaiian guitar (or electric guitar)

grow - in' like a breeze. Coun - try roads take me home to the place I be - long: West Vir - gin - ia moun - tain mom - ma, take me home coun - try roads.

**12**

If you have a 44, or a 49 note keyboard, these will be your top three notes.

I have placed letter names beside the new notes in the next few songs.

## SAILING

Words & Music by Gavin Sutherland

**Suggested registration:** jazz organ
+ sustain

**Rhythm:** disco
**Tempo:** slow ( ♩ = 69); but run rhythm at double speed
( ♩ = 138)
Synchro-start, if available

I am sail - ing, I am sail - ing, home a-

gain _____ 'cross the sea. I am sail - ing storm-y

wa - ters to be near _____ you, to be free. I am

\* Pause on each note, for dramatic effect.

# SPANISH EYES

**Words by Charles Singleton & Eddie Snyder**
**Music by Bert Kaempfert**

**Suggested registration:** string ensemble

**Rhythm:** tango (or beguine)
**Tempo:** medium ( ♩ = 108)

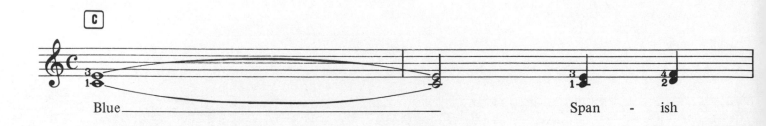

Blue _____ Span - ish

eyes, _____ tear - drops are fall - ing

Tuck thumb under 4th finger

from your Span - ish eyes.

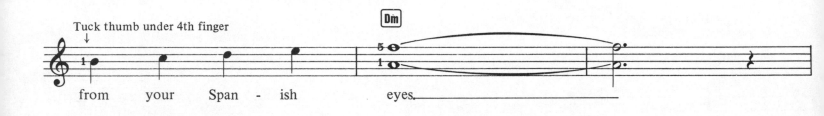

Please _____ please don't cry.

_____ This is just a - dios and not good

bye._____  Soon_____

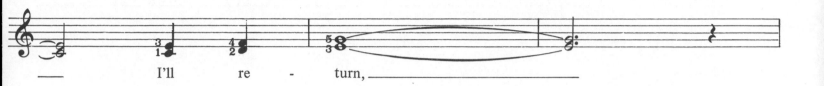

\_\_ I'll re - turn,_____

bring-ing you all the love your heart can hold._____

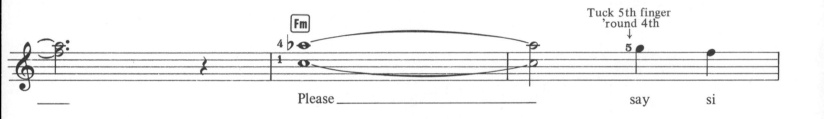

\_\_ Please _____ say si

si,_____ say you and your Span - ish

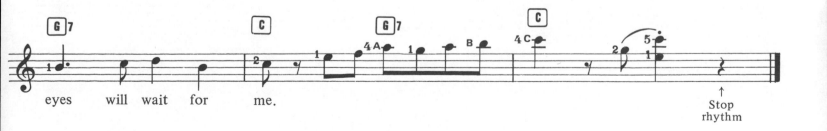

eyes will wait for me.

# CRUISING DOWN THE RIVER

Words & Music by Eily Beadell & Nell Tollerton

**Suggested registration:** accordion

**Rhythm:** waltz
**Tempo:** fairly fast ( ♩ = 152)

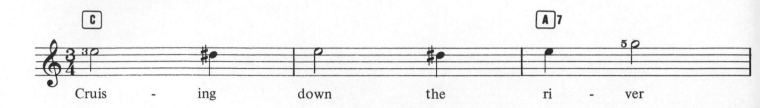

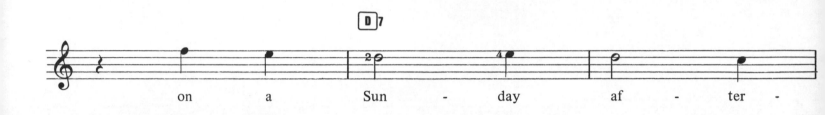

Cruis - ing down the ri - ver

on a Sun - day af - ter -

noon. With one you

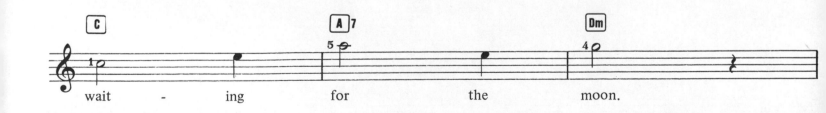

love, the sun a - bove,

wait - ing for the moon.

The old ac - cord - ion
two of us to -

play - ing_____ a sen - ti -
geth - er_____ we'll plan a

men - tal tune.
hon - ey - moon.

Cruis - ing down the riv - er,
Cruis - ing down the riv - er,

on a Sun - day af - ter -
on a

noon. The birds a -

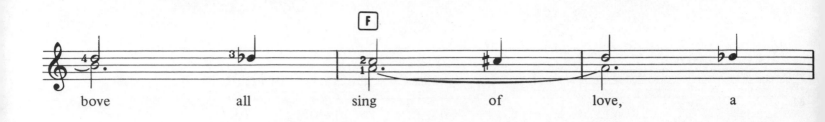

bove      all      sing      of      love,      a

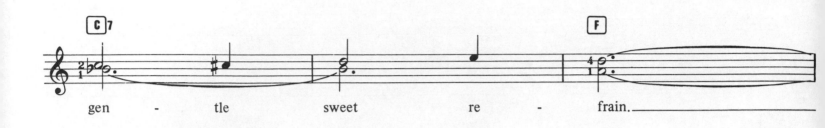

gen - tle      sweet      re - frain._____

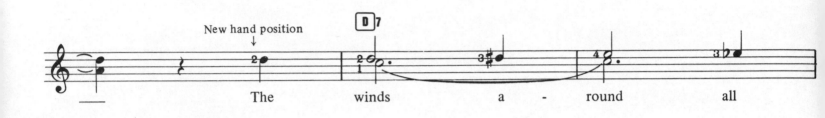

New hand position

The      winds      a - round      all

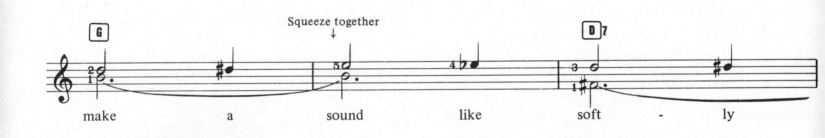

Squeeze together

make      a      sound      like      soft - ly

flute to accordion      *D.S. al CODA*

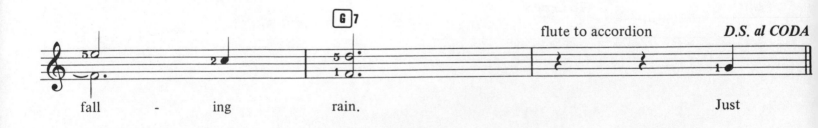

fall - ing      rain.      Just

CODA

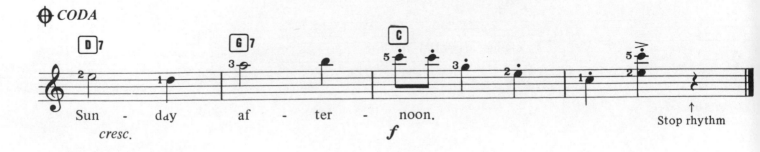

Sun - day      af - ter - noon.

*cresc.*      *f*      Stop rhythm

# HELLO GOODBYE

Words & Music by John Lennon & Paul McCartney

**Suggested registration:** electric guitar

**Rhythm:** rock
**Tempo:** medium ( ♩ = 112)

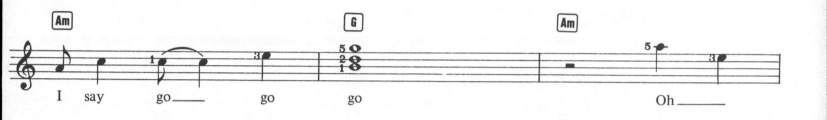

You say yes___ I say no___ you say stop___ and

I say go___ go go Oh___

no. You say good-bye, and I say hel-

lo, Hel-lo, hel-lo. I don't know why you say good-bye, I say hel-

lo, Hel-lo, hel-lo. I don't know why you say good-bye, I say hel-lo.

# LAST WORD

**13**

Congratulations on reaching the end of Book Two of The Complete Keyboard Player.

In Book Three you will

- improve your note reading
- learn new chords
- play in new keys, including "minor" keys
- develop further your sense of rhythm
- add those important professional touches to your playing.

# CHORD CHART (Showing all "fingered chords" used in the course so far)

**14**

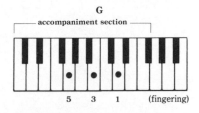

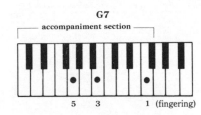

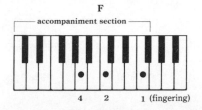

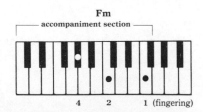

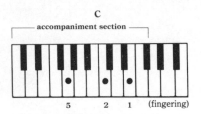

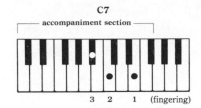

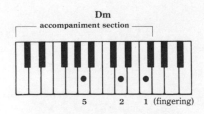

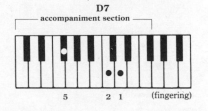

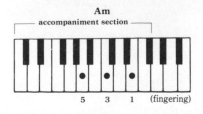

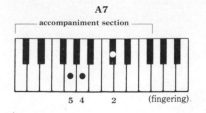

12/89 (9718)